FAMOUS SONGS of WALES 1 CANEUON ENWOG CYMRU

9020

Trefnwyd gan/*Arranged by*

JOHN HYWEL

GWYNN
Penygroes, Caernarfon,
Gwynedd LL54 6DB.

CYDNABOD

Dymunir diolch i Fwrdd Croeso Cymru am gael defnyddio lluniau lliw o'u heiddo. Diolchir i Fanc Midland ccc am nawdd ariannol tuag at gynhyrchu'r llyfr hwn.

ACKNOWLEDGEMENTS

The Publishers wish to thank the Wales Tourist Board for the use of colour photographs in this publication. The Publishers wish to acknowledge the support of the Midland Bank plc in preparing this publication.

Clawr: Castell Harlech.
Cover: Harlech castle.

ISBN: 0 900426 60 8

Cerddoriaeth/Music: MSS Studios, 102 Ameysford Rd., Ferndown, Dorset, BH22 9QE.
Argraffwyd/Printed: Gwasg Dwyfor, Penygroes.

FOREWORD

We hope you will enjoy singing these Songs of Wales and that they will remind you of our beautiful country.

Wales has been called the "Land of Song" and it is true that singing has always been an important feature of our culture.

We have endeavoured to include here a varied sample of our music — old harp airs to which words have been added at one time or another; old folk dances; lullabies and nursery rhymes; military music; and love songs. And we have only lightly scratched the surface! Much more material is available.

The music has been arranged by our Music Editor, Mr John Hywel, who has tried to keep the arrangements as simple as possible so that you need not be an experienced pianist to be able to play, — for your own pleasure as well as for your friends' delight.

We hope that the collection brings you many happy moments.

CYNNWYS *CONTENTS*

HEN WLAD FY NHADAU
THE LAND OF MY FATHERS

Geiriau Cymraeg — Evan James
English Words — W. S. Gwynn Williams

Trefnwyd gan / *Arranged by*
John Hywel ©

Yn urddasol/*With dignity*

Piano and/or S.A.T.B.

Mae hen wlad fy nha-dau yn an-nwyl i___ mi, Gwlad
The land of my fa-thers is dear un-to___ me, Old

beirdd a chan-tor-ion, en-wog-ion o fri; Ei gw-rol ry-
land where the mins-trels are hon-oured and free; Its war-ring de-

-fel-wyr, gwlad-gar-wyr tra___ mad, Tros rydd-id coll-as-ant eu
-fen-ders, so___ gall-ant and___ brave, For free-dom their life's blood they

gwaed. Gwlad, gwlad, pleid-iol wyf___ i'm gwlad, Tra môr yn
gave. Wales, Wales, true___ am I___ to Wales, While seas se-

fur i'r bur hoff___ bau, O bydd-ed i'r hen-iaith bar-hau.
-cure this land so___ pure, O may our old lang-uage en-dure.

The National Anthem of Wales

Our National Anthem is the result of co-operation between father and son. It is said that a weaver from Pontypridd in Glamorgan, Evan James, wrote the words one Sunday morning in January 1856 to a tune composed by his son, James James, and which was possibly based on an old harp melody. The music was first published in *Gems of Welsh Melody* 1860.

Dr Percy Scholes, the eminent musician, described the song as "the most noble anthem possessed by any nation."

The English translation in this book is by W. S. Gwynn Williams of Llangollen, founder of the Gwynn Publishing Company, and follow closely the original Welsh.

The air is also sung as the Breton Anthem, to words by the native poet, Taldir.

Codiad haul, Yr Wyddfa. *Sunrise, Snowdon.*

GWŶR HARLECH
MEN OF HARLECH

Geiriau Cymraeg — Ceiriog
English Words — G. J. W.

Trefnwyd gan / *Arranged by*
John Hywel ©

We — le goel — certh wen yn fflam — io, A tha — fo — dau tân yn bloedd — io,
Gan fan-llef — au'r tyw — ys — o — gion, Llais gel — yn — ion, trwst ar — fo — gion,
O'er the hills, though night lies sleep — ing, Tongues of flame through mists are leap — ing,
At the call, from glen and vall — ey, Now the watch — ful war — riors rall — y,

Ymdeithgan gyflym/*Quick march*

Ar i'r dew — rion ddod i da — ro Un-waith et — o'n un;
A char — lam — iad y march — ogion, Craig ar graig a grŷn!
As the brave, their vi — gil keep — ing, Front the dead — ly fray;
And with wa — ry foot-steps sall — y Forth in full arr — ay.

Cwym — pa llaw — er llyw — ydd, Ar — fon byth ni or — fydd,
Then the batt — le thun — der Tears the rocks as — un — der,

Cyrff y gel — yn wrth y cant or — ffwy — sant — yn — y — ffos — ydd;
As the light falls on the flight of foes — with — out — their — plun — der;

Yng ngo — leu — ni'r goel — certh ac — w, Tros we — fu — sau Cym — ro'n ma — rw,
There the van — quished horde is rout — ed; There the — val — iant ne — ver doubt — ed,

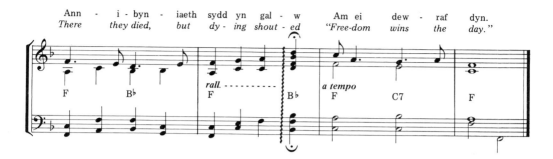

2. Ni chaiff gelyn ladd ac ymlid,
   Harlech, Harlech cwyd i'w herlid;
   Y mae Rhoddwr Mawr Ein Rhyddid
   Yn rhoi nerth i ni;
   Wele Gymru a'i byddinoedd
   Yn ymdywallt o'r mynyddoedd,
   Rhuthrant fel rhaeadrau dyfroedd,
   Llamant fel y lli;
   Llwyddiant i'n llywyddion,
   Rwystro bâr yr estron,
   Gwybod yn ei galon gaiff
   Fel bratha cleddyf Brython;
   Cledd yn erbyn cledd a chwery,
   Dur yn erbyn dur a dery,
   Wele faner Gwalia i fyny,
   Rhyddid aiff â hi.

2. *Those who come to slay and pillage*
   Never waste nor win a village;
   God, who blesses toil and tillage,
   Gave us men of might;
   When agressor hosts are nearing,
   Stand the men who know no fearing,
   Who, to hearth and home adhering,
   Never shirk the fight;
   Steadfast in endeavour,
   Wills that waver never,
   Hearts that love and hands that hew,
   And fame that lives for ever;
   While the storms of all the ages,
   While the work of ruin rages,
   They shall paint the proudest pages
   In the roll of Right.

Harlech, a small town on the west coast of Meirionnydd in North Wales, is dominated by the castle built in the 13th century by Edward I.

Whether or not this march dates back to that time is not known, but the Welsh music historian, Mr Huw Williams, Bangor, states that it was first published in 1784 by Edward Jones in London.

One thing is certain — it is among the best-known of Welsh airs and is generally sung to the Welsh words given here, although there are many other versions and paraphrases.

The famous musician, Dr Crotch, considered the military music of Wales to be superior to that of any other nation.

Not everyone remembers that Harlech also features in one of the oldest of Welsh legends, the story of Brân, "King of the Isle of the Mighty", a legend dating back possibly to pre-Roman times. It was on this rock that he and his court watched the fleet of the King of Ireland sailing into Britain, the sea at that time lapping the foot of the rock.

RHYFELGYRCH CAPTEN MORGAN
CAPTAIN MORGAN'S MARCH

Geiriau Cymraeg — E. Nicholson Jones
English Words — Dewi Môn

Trefnwyd gan / *Arranged by*
John Hywel ©

2. Heidia ysbrydion arwyr Cymru Fu,
   Ar ein mynyddau draw yn llu,
   Fel pe yn gwylio ffawd ein baner wen;
   Daliwn hon yn wrol tua'r nen;
   Taer weddiau ddyrchant ar ein rhan.
   Bloeddiwn fuddugoliaeth yn y man;
   Ddewrion Cymru! Duw'n ein pleidio
   sydd,
   Fe geir gweled Cymru yn Gymru rydd.

2. *Far up the mountains shrouded in
   the mist,
   Spirits of warriors still resist,
   Ever beseeching that their sons maintain
   Cambria's proud banner free from stain;
   Wives and mothers virtuous and true,
   Whom you are defending, pray God
   for you;
   Home in triumph you'll return ere long,
   Surely as the right must defeat
   the wrong.*

It is not certain who the 'Morgan' in the song's title was. He could have been one of the leaders of a revolt against the heavy taxes levied by Edward I of England about 1294, but the first published record of the music only dates back to 1784, when it appeared in *Musical and Poetical Relicks of the Welsh Bards,* published in London.

It is interesting to note that this air is also sung to honour the winning Bards at the Crowning and Chairing Ceremonies at the National Eisteddfod of Wales each August, and that this practice is followed by many other eisteddfodau.

Seremoni'r Orsedd, Eisteddfod Genedlaethol. *Gorsedd ceremony, National Eisteddfod.*

DAFYDD Y GARREG WEN
DAVID OF THE WHITE ROCK

Geiriau Cymraeg — Ceiriog
English Words — J. Gwilym Jones (Bangor)

Trefnwyd gan / *Arranged by*
John Hywel ©

"Car - iwch" medd___ Daf - ydd "fy nhel - yn___ i___ mi, _____
"Bring___ me," said___ Dav - id, "my harp___ where___ I___ lie, _____

Yn drist/Sadly

Ceis - iaf cyn mar - w___ roi tôn ar - ni hi.
I wish to play one___ last air be - fore I die;

Co - dwch___ fy nwy - lo___ i gyr - raedd___ y___ tant, _____
Lift my___ weak arms, lay___ my___ hands to___ the___ strings, _____

Duw___ a'ch ben - dith - io___ fy ngwedd - w a'm plant".
May___ you, ___ my___ loved___ ones, be kept___ 'neath God's wings."

2. Neithiwr mi glywais lais angel fel hyn:
   "Dafydd, tyrd adref a chwarae drwy'r
   glyn."
   Delyn fy mebyd! ffarwel i dy dant,
   Duw a'ch bendithio, fy ngweddw a'm
   plant.

2. *Last night an angel came near me to say,*
   "David, come home now, and, as you
   come, play."
   Harp of my youth! Farewell, strings of
   my life,
   May God now bless you, my children,
   my wife.

Tradition has it that, on his deathbed, the old harpist Dafydd, called for his beloved harp and played this lovely air, asking for it to be sung at his funeral.

Dafydd would also have been a *bard*, for bard-harpists were important leaders of the community in which they lived.

Whatever the traditions, fact has it that the air is at least 200 years old, for it was first published in 1784 in *Relicks of the Welsh Bards.*

The Welsh harp was rather different from the pedal harp which is generally seen today. It was a triple-stringed instrument, with the left hand, not the right, playing the melody. That harp is still in use today by some harpists.

The farm *Y Garreg Wen* is situated not far from Porthmadog, Gwynedd, at one time a busy slate port and now a popular holiday resort.

HIRAETH
TELL ME, WISE-MEN

Geiriau Cymraeg — Traddodiadol
English Words — J. Gwilym Jones (Bangor)

Trefnwyd gan / *Arranged by*
John Hywel ©

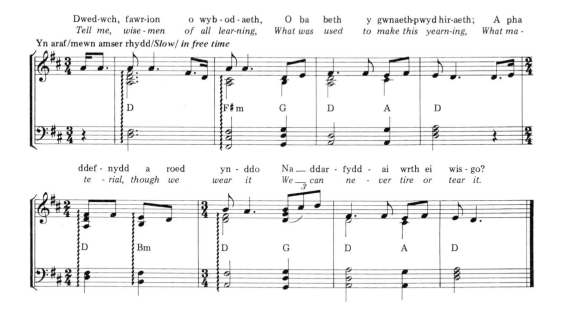

Hiraeth

Dwedwch, fawrion o wybodaeth,
O ba beth y gwnaethpwyd hiraeth;
A pha ddefnydd a roed ynddo
Na ddarfyddai wrth ei wisgo?

Derfydd aur a derfydd arian,
Derfydd melfed, derfydd sidan;
Derfydd pob dilledyn helaeth,
Eto er hyn ni dderfydd hiraeth.

Hiraeth mawr a hiraeth creulon,
Hiraeth sydd yn torri 'nghalon,
Pan fwy' dryma'r nos yn cysgu
Fe ddaw hiraeth ac a'm deffry.

Hiraeth, hiraeth, cilia, cilia,
Paid â phwyso mor drwm arna',
Nesa dipyn at yr erchwyn,
Gad i mi gael cysgu gronyn.

Fe gwn yr haul, fe gwn y lleuad,
Fe gwn y môr yn donnau irad,
Fe gwn y gwynt yn uchel ddigon,
Ni chwn yr Hiraeth byth o'r galon.

Tell Me, Wise-men

Tell me, wise-men of all learning,
What was used to make this yearning,
What material, though we wear it
We can never tire or tear it.

Finest silks and satins perish,
Silver, gold and things we cherish,
But there is no rust nor burning
Nor even time to touch this yearning.

Yearning cruel, cold, unspoken,
Yearning haunts me till I'm broken;
When at last in sleep I'm turning
There to wake me comes this yearning.

Yearning, yearning, go behind me,
Please don't try so hard to find me;
Give me room till I am stronger,
Let me sleep a little longer.

Suns shall rise, and moons so soundless,
Winds shall rise, their freedom boundless,
Waves shall rise when seas are churning,
But not my heart from 'neath this yearning.

Every language has words which are almost impossible to translate. *Hiraeth* is one of those words in the Welsh language, and is often rendered in English as 'longing' or 'nostalgia' or 'yearning'. Matthew Arnold is one critic who maintains that *Hiraeth* is a characteristic of the Celtic races.

However, the emotions conveyed by those words are nowhere as potent as that of *Hiraeth*, which one could almost say is a feeling of near physical sickness, — that deep emptiness felt by all who suffer some traumatic experience such as losing a loved one, or being forced to leave home, as so many Welsh people have done during the past 200 years. Perhaps this is why home-coming exiles love to sing one of the many songs touching upon *Hiraeth*.

This particular melody is an Anglesey folk-tune collected by Dr J. Lloyd Williams, one of the founders of the Welsh Folk Song Society early this century. The author of the words given here is unknown, and are not the only ones sung to this tune. This type of song was usually sung unaccompanied, although that is not always the case today.

AR LAN Y MÔR
UPON THE SHORE

Geiriau Cymraeg — Traddodiadol
English Words — J. Gwilym Jones (Bangor)

Trefnwyd gan / *Arranged by*
John Hywel ©

2. Ar lan y môr mae carreg wastad,
   Lle bûm yn siarad gair â'm cariad;
   O amgylch hon fe dyf y lili
   Ac ambell gangen o rosmari.

3. Ar lan y môr mae cerrig gleision,
   Ar lan y môr mae blodau'r meibion,
   Ar lan y môr mae pob rhinweddau,
   Ar lan y môr mae 'nghariad innau.

2. *Upon the shore, through wind and weather,*
   A stone, where once we talked together,
   Has now white lilies near it showing
   And shoots of fragrant rosemary growing.

3. *Upon the shore blue stones abounding,*
   Upon the shore fine youths surrounding,
   But of all joys I there discover
   Upon the shore, I have a lover.

Little is known of the history of this lovely plaintive melody, which was first published as recently as 1937 by the Welsh Folk Song Society. The air is, of course, much older, and was certainly used in unaccompanied singing — maybe to extempore verses by local poets at various social gatherings in hamlets and farmhouses.

The words used here are traditional and are typical of a certain form of Welsh verse, with words being constantly repeated for poetic effect. The poet fancies seeing all manner of beautiful sights by the sea shore, the most beautiful being his beloved.

Bae Barafundle, Sir Benfro. *Barafundle Bay, Pembrokeshire.*

LLWYN ONN
THE ASH GROVE

Geiriau Cymraeg — Geirallt Jones
English Words — Y. Oliphant

Trefnwyd gan / *Arranged by*
John Hywel ©

Yn Nyf - fryn Llwyn Onn draw mi we - lais hardd
Gwyn ew - yn y lli oedd ei gwisg, a dis-
Down yon - der green val - ley where stream - lets me-
Or at the bright moon - tide in sol - i - tude

Mewn amser Miniwet/*In Minuet time*

fein - wen A min - nau'n ham - dde - na 'rôl byw ar y don;
gleir - wen, A'r glas - for oedd llyg - aid Gwen hardd - af Llwyn Onn.
- an - der, When twi - light is fa - ding I pens - ive - ly rove;
wan - der, A - mid the dark shades of the lone - ly Ash Grove;

A — nin - nau'n — rhod - ian - na drwy'r lon - ydd — i'r ban - na, Si -
'Twas — there, while — the black - bird was cheer - ful - ly — sing - ing, I

bryd - em — i'n — gi - lydd gyf - ri - nach byd serch; A
first met — that — dear one the joy of my heart! A-

phan ddaeth hi'n — ad - eg ffar - we - lio — â'r wiw deg, Roedd
round us for — glad - ness the blue - bells — were — ring - ing, Ah!

2. Cyn dychwel i borthladd wynebwn
   y tonnau,
   Ond hyfryd yw'r hafan 'rôl dicter y don;
   Bydd melys anghofio her greulon
   y creigiau —
   Un felly o'wn innau 'rôl cyrraedd
   Llwyn Onn.
   A thawel mordwyo wnaf mwyach
   â Gwenno
   Yn llong fach ein bwthyn a hi wrth
   y llyw;
   A hon fydd yr hafan ddiogel a chryno
   I'r morwr a'i Wenno tra byddwn ni byw.

2. Still glows the bright sunshine o'er
   valley and mountain,
   Still warbles the blackbird its note
   from the tree;
   Still trembles the moonbeam on
   streamlet and fountain,
   But what are the beauties of Nature
   to me?
   With sorrow, deep sorrow, my bosom
   is laden,
   All day I go mourning in search of
   my love!
   Ye echoes! oh, tell me, where is the
   sweet maiden?
   "She sleeps 'neath the green turf
   down by the Ash Grove."

This is a very old harp melody, and was first published without words by Edward Jones (The King's Harpist) in *The Bardic Museum* in 1802. It was published with words, probably some four years later, in *Welsh Melodies with Appropriate English Words*.

Some authorities maintain that it was originally a dance tune. If that is so, it does not appear to be as old as some of the well-known traditional folk dances, as the minuet time is of a later period, originating in 18th Century France.

During this century it has been a popular counter-melody for that unique Welsh practice of Penillion singing.

The Welsh words used here are of recent date, relating a sailor's love for Gwen of Llwyn Onn. Oliphant's English words, however, end with sadness, relating the death of the loved one.

CROEN Y DDAFAD FELAN
ROUND THE YELLOW SHEEPSKIN

Geiriau Cymraeg — Ceiriog
English Words — J. Gwilym Jones (Bangor)

Trefnwyd gan / *Arranged by*
John Hywel ©

Croen y ddaf - ad fel — an   Tu - a 'chwyn - eb all — an,
Spread the sheep - skin out, lads, Change and step a - bout, lads,

Cyflym gyda sigl /*Fast and rhythmic*

F   Gm   F

Troed yn ôl, a throed ym - laen, A ph'run di'r ol - a rw — an?
One foot on and one foot back And kick one foot right out, lads.

C7   F   B♭   C

Croen y ddaf - ad fel — an   Tu - a 'chwyn - eb all — an,
Round the yel - low sheep - skin, Ov - er two pipes wheel - ing,

F   Gm   F

Troed yn ôl, a throed ym - laen, A throed i gic - io'r nen - bran.
One foot up and one foot down And one to kick the cei - ling.

Gm   F   C7   F

This old harp air, dating back at least to 1703 when it was published by Playford, is a popular folk dance tune. It is generally danced by parties in multiples of eight, and is known as a 'longways progressive dance'.

The air is also used as a solo clog dance for men, using a broom stick for 'kicking over', and a lighted candle in a bottle. An experienced dancer will never accidentally extinguish the candle! The solo dance is attributed to a shepherd on the Berwyn Mountains in Clwyd.

The Welsh words are by Llew Tegid, a famous eisteddfod compére who died in 1928, and refer to the steps followed by the dancers. The words, of course, are not used when dancing!

Bugeilio yn Rhandir-mwyn. *Sheep farming, Rhandir-mwyn.*

NOS GALAN
ON ITS WAY THE OLD YEAR HURRIES

Geiriau Cymraeg — Traddodiadol
English Words — J. Gwilym Jones (Bangor)

Trefnwyd gan / *Arranged by*
John Hywel ©

Oer yw'r gŵr sy'n meth-u car-u, Ffal, la, la, la, la, la, la, la, la.
On its way the old year hur-ries, Fal, la, la, la, la, la, la, la, la.

Yn llawen/*Bright and joyful*

Hen fyn-ydd-oedd ann-wyl Cym-ru, Ffal, la, la, la, la, la, la, la, la.
Let it take our cares and wor-ries, Fal, la, la, la, la, la, la, la, la.

Idd-o ef a'u câr gyn-hes-af, Ffal, la, la, la, la, la, la, la.
May the new year bring its treas-ure Fal, la, la, la, la, la, la, la.

Gwyl-iau llaw-en flwydd-yn nes-af, Ffal, la, la, la, la, la, la, la, la.
Full of wealth and joy and pleas-ure. Fal, la, la, la, la, la, la, la, la.

The air as we know it dates back some 200 years, and many different words have been sung to it from time to time, always reflecting the social customs of a rural community.

Long ago, the tune was very popular at 'get-togethers' with farm workers, when local poets would sing verses of their own composition, relating their neighbours' misadventures, much to the joy of some and the mortification of others! The chorus of "ffa-la-la" would be sung by all present.

The title emphasises the importance previously placed on New Year's Eve in Wales — New Year's Day being of greater significance than Christmas Day until the early years of this century. Many traditions are associated with the New Year, such as that of the hunting of the wren.

The Welsh words used here are by Ceiriog, and were composed specially for *Songs of Wales*, 1874, where he maintains that anyone not loving his native mountains must indeed have a cold heart.

Castell Caerffili. *Caerphilly Castle.*

Y MOCHYN DU
THE BLACK PIG

Geiriau Cymraeg — John Owen
English Words — Sir H. Idris Bell

Trefnwyd gan / *Arranged by*
John Hywel ©

Rhedodd Deio i Lwyncelyn,
I gael Mati at y Mochyn,
Dwedodd Mati wrtho'n union
Gall'sai roi ef heibio'n burion.
   O! mor drwm, etc.

Gweithiwyd iddo arch o dderi,
Wedi ei drimio a'i berarogli;
Ac fe dorrwyd bedd ardderchog
I'r hen fochyn yng Ngharngoediog.
   O! mor drwm, etc.

Y Parchedig Wil Twm Griffi
Ydoedd yno yn pregethu;
Pawb yn sobor anghyffredin,
Oll i ddangos parch i'r Mochyn.
   O! mor drwm, etc.

Bellach 'rydwyf yn terfynu
'Nawr gan roddi heibio ganu,
Cymrwch ofal bawb rhag dilyn
Siampl ddrwg wrth fwydo mochyn.
   O! mor drwm, etc.

Deio, running to Llwyncelyn,
Fetched old Matty to the Mochyn;
Matty swore he'd ne'er recover,
Sure and certain all was over.
   O! how sad of heart are we, etc.

Then we bought a polished coffin,
Silver knobs and velvet trimming;
And a vault with bricks and mortar
In the churchyard we did order.
   O! how sad of heart are we, etc.

Then the Reverend Thomas Griffiths
Came to read the funeral service;
Everyone was sad and sobbing
At the funeral of our Mochyn.
   O! how sad of heart are we, etc.

Now my friends, my song is ended,
Note the warning I've intended —
Mind you act with great discretion
When you go to feed your Mochyn.
   O! how sad of heart are we, etc.

This popular humorous ballad could perhaps be called "The Lament for the late Black Pig", and is sung to the tune of *Lili Lon*. Although in a light vein, it does emphasise the importance of the pig in a poor rural farming community.

The original words were composed by John Owen, a farm labourer who later became a nonconformist minister. They record the 'loss' of a pig belonging to a neighbour, David Morris.

There are any number of stanzas, varying from place to place in different parts of Wales, but always with the same refrain, sung with mock grief for the dead 'mochyn'.

The tune was also used by ballad singers at fairs and similar gatherings. Ballad singers, in Wales as in England, were important conveyers of news before the advent of the popular newspapers, and were considered as commentators on 'the way of the world'.

The few verses given here give the gist of the story, and Sir Idris Bell's English translation is very close to the original.

DACW MAM YN DWAD
HURRY, HURRY MOTHER

Geiriau Cymraeg — Traddodiadol
English Words — Megan Morris

Trefnwyd gan / *Arranged by*
John Hywel ©

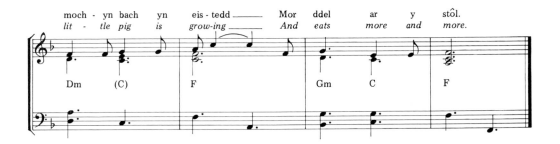

moch - yn bach yn eis - tedd _____ Mor ddel ar y stôl.
lit - tle pig is grow-ing _____ And eats more and more.

Dm (C) F Gm C F

2. Dafi bach a minne
   Yn mynd i Aberdâr;
   Dafi'n mofyn ceiliog
   A minne'n mofyn iâr.
   Shoni Bric a Moni
   Yn mofyn buwch a llo,
   A merlyn bach a mochyn
   A cheiliog go-go-go.
   Ceiliog bach y Dandi
   Yn crio drwy y nos,
   Eisiau menthyg ceiniog
   I brynu gwasgod goch.

2. *Aberdare is handy*
   Tomorrow we'll be there,
   Davy wants some hens and
   A rooster at the fair.
   Lanky John and Monnie
   Need a cob or two,
   As well as cows and calves
   And a cock-a-doodle-doo.
   "I must have a jerkin.
   The colour must be red,
   Or else I'll crow to spite you
   All night," the bantam said.

This well-loved nursery-rhyme is as popular today as ever it was, perhaps on account of its lilting rhythm.

Little is known of its history other than that it probably originated in north west Wales. The second verse is a later addition and obviously belongs to the south Wales valleys.

Megan Morris' English translation conveys very well the happy 'no-sense' words of the original.

Machlud haul, Llyn Cregennen. *Sunset, Llyn Cregennen.*

SUO-GÂN
LULLABY

Geiriau Cymraeg — Robert Bryan
English Words — T. G. J. (Edited)

Trefnwyd gan / *Arranged by*
John Hywel ©

Hun - a, blen-tyn, ar fy myn-wes, Clyd a chyn-nes yd - yw hon;
Sleep my dar-ling, on my bo-som, Harm will ne-ver come to you;

Sigl araf/With gentle rocking motion

Breich - iau mam sy'n dynn am-dan-at, Car - iad mam sy dan fy mron.
Moth - er's arms en - fold you safe-ly, Moth - er's heart is e - ver true.

Ni cha' dim am - har - u'th gyn-tun, Ni wna un-dyn â thi gam;
As you sleep there's nought to scare you, Nought to wake you from your rest;

Hun - a'n da-wel, ann - wyl blen-tyn, Hun - a'n fwyn ar fron dy fam.
Close those eye-lids, lit - tle an-gel, Sleep up - on your moth-er's breast.

2. Huna'n dawel heno, huna,
   Huna'n fwyn, y tlws ei lun;
   Pam yr wyt yn awr yn gwenu,
   Gwenu'n dirion yn dy hun?
   Ai angylion fry sy'n gwenu
   Arnat ti yn gwenu'n llon,
   Tithau'n gwenu'n ôl dan huno,
   Huno'n dawel ar fy mron?

3. Paid ag ofni, dim ond deilen
   Gura, gura ar y ddôr;
   Paid ag ofni, ton fach unig
   Sua, sua ar lan y môr.
   Huna, blentyn, nid oes yma
   Ddim i roddi i ti fraw;
   Gwena'n dawel yn fy mynwes
   Ar yr engyl gwynion draw.

2. *Sleep, my darling, night is falling*
   Rest in slumber sound and deep;
   I would know why you are smiling,
   Smiling sweetly as you sleep!
   Do you see the angels smiling
   As they see your rosy rest,
   So that you must smile an answer
   As you slumber on my breast?

3. *Don't be frightened, it's a leaflet*
   Tapping, tapping on the door;
   Don't be frightened, 'twas a wavelet,
   Sighing, sighing on the shore.
   Slumber, slumber, nought can hurt you,
   Nothing bring you harm or fright,
   Slumber, darling, smiling sweetly
   At those angels robed in white.

The Welsh words are by the late Robert Bryan (Caernarfon and Cairo) who notes that the melody was taken from an old book in the possession of Mr Orwig Williams, Llanberis. The words are a mother's assurance to her baby that he may safely sleep in her bosom — there is nothing but the wind rustling the leaves by the door to worry him.

It is probable, however, that Welsh mothers would sing the tune to their children even 200 or 300 years ago, and one tradition has it that the infant son of Edward I had a Welsh nurse who sang it to the baby.

The tune has been set and arranged for many choirs and soloists, and is in the repertoire of the famous choir of St. John's College, Cambridge, who sing it in the original Welsh.

BUGEILIO'R GWENITH GWYN
WATCHING THE WHEAT

Geiriau Cymraeg — Wil Hopcyn
English Words — J. R. & T. G. J. (Edited)

Trefnwyd gan / *Arranged by*
John Hywel ©

Mi sydd fach - gen ieu - anc ffôl Yn byw yn ôl fy ffan - si, My-
I'm a fool - ish love -sick lad And live my life so free-ly; I

Yn llyfn/With flowing motion

D   A7 D   D   D   (D7)

fi'n bu - gei - lio'r gwe - nith gwyn, Ac ar - all yn ei fe - di.
watch and tend the grow-ing wheat While oth-ers har - vest gai - ly. I

G   D   G   A   D

Pam na ddeu - i ar fy ôl, Ryw ddydd ar ôl ei gi - lydd? Gwaith
pray you, come to me, my love, So we may be to - ge - ther. I

D   G   E   A   D7

'rwy'n dy weld, y fei - nir fach, Yn lan - nach, lan - nach beu - nydd.
vow that with each day that dawns You are to me the fair - er.

G   (A7) F#m   (B) Em   A   D

2. Glannach, glannach wyt bob dydd,
   Neu fi yn wir sy'n ffolach;
   Er mwyn y Gŵr a wnaeth dy wedd
   Dod im' drugaredd bellach.
   Cwnn dy ben, gwel acw draw,
   Rho im' dy law wen dirion;
   Gwaith yn dy fynwes bert ei thro
   Mae allwedd clo fy nghalon.

3. Tra fo dŵr y môr yn hallt,
   A thra bo gallt yn tyfu,
   A thra fo calon dan fy mron
   Mi fydda'n ffyddlon iti;
   Dywed imi'r gwir heb gêl,
   A rho dan sêl d'atebion,
   P'un ai myfi ai arall, Ann
   Sydd orau gan dy galon.

2. *I'm a foolish love-lorn lad*
   Who lives his life so freely;
   I watch and tend the growing wheat
   While others harvest gaily.
   I pray you, come to me, my love,
   That we may be together.
   I vow that with each day that dawns
   You are to me the fairer.

3. *While the ocean waves are salt,*
   And while the hills wear heather,
   And while a heart within me pounds,
   I vow true love for ever.
   Tell me truly, I implore, —
   And give your word sincerely, —
   If it be I or someone else
   You love, dear Ann, most dearly.

This beautiful harp air, a favourite of many world-renowned singers, is usually sung to words attributed to a young poet named Wil Hopcyn from Glamorgan in South Wales.

Wil and a local heiress, Ann Thomas, were deeply in love, but her father forbade Ann from seeing Wil and forced her to marry the son of a neighbouring squire. It is said that Wil composed the words and sent them to Ann surreptitiously. As in all good love stories, the young girl pined away and eventually died.

The story has been captured in verse by the 19th century poet, Ceiriog, with English translation by Prof. T. Gwynn Jones.

AR HYD Y NOS
ALL THROUGH THE NIGHT

Geiriau Cymraeg — Ceiriog
English Words — J. Gwilym Jones (Bangor)

Trefnwyd gan / *Arranged by*
John Hywel ©

2. O mor siriol gwena seren,
   Ar hyd y nos.
   I oleuo'i chwaer-ddaearen,
   Ar hyd y nos.
   Nos yw henaint pan ddaw cystudd, —
   Ond i harddu dyn a'i hwyrddydd,
   Rhown ein golau gwan i'n gilydd,
   Ar hyd y nos.

2. *When our world lies dark in sadness*
   All through the night,
   Every star smiles down its gladness
   All through the night;
   So our friends in pain or sorrow,
   Waiting for that far tomorrow,
   Rays of hope from us may borrow
   All through the night.

Here is one of the most tranquil of Welsh airs, dating back to the middle of the 18th Century. It was at one time also known as "Poor Mary Ann".

The playwright Alan Ayckbourn makes use of the song in his play *A Chorus of Disapproval*, being the tale of an amateur production of Gay's "The Beggar's Opera." It is a fact that Gay used the melody in his famous 'opera'.

Today the tune is very popular with male voice choirs, and has been arranged for them by some of our most eminent musicians. These arrangements have been sung, not only at the 1,000-Voices Festival at the Royal Albert Hall, London, but also in such foreign cities as Sydney, Bonn, Vancouver and New York.

Although the Welsh words given here are not the only ones sung to this tune, they are by far the most well-known. The English translation by John Gwilym Jones, Bangor, is a new one prepared especially for this publication.